Keep on Counting

Helping your child

- Remember that the activities in this book should be enjoyed by your child. Try to find a quiet place to work.
- Your child does not need to complete each page in one go. Always stop before your child grows tired and come back to the same page another time.
- It is important to work through the pages in the right order because the activities get progressively more difficult.
- The activities in this book cover counting up to 20, reading and writing numerals, ordering numbers, and an introduction to adding and taking away.
- The answers to the activities are on page 32.
- Always give your child lots of encouragement and praise.
- Remember that the gold stars are a reward for effort as well as for achievement.

This edition published by Parragon Books Ltd in 2017

Parragon Books Ltd
Chartist House
15-17 Trim Street
Bath BA1 1HA, UK
www.parragon.com

Written by Nina Filipek
Illustrated by Simon Abbot and Adam Linley
Educational Consultant: Geraldine Taylor

ISBN: 978-1-4748-7614-8

Printed in China

Contents

Counting up to 3

Count the kittens. Touch each kitten as you count it.

Colour a bowl for each kitten.
How many bowls do you need?
Write the correct number in the box.

Point to each number as you count it.

Note for parent: Point to 0 on the number line. Tell your child that zero means 'none'. Ask: 'How many dogs can you count in the picture?' (There are none!)

Counting up to 5

Count the chicks. Touch each chick as you count it.

Colour a nest for each chick.
How many nests do you need?
Write the correct number in the box.

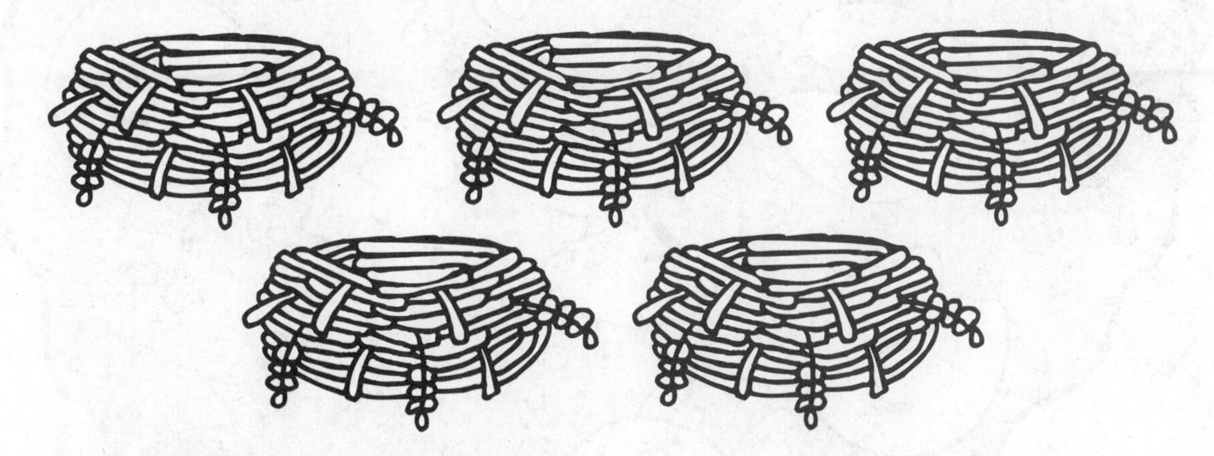

Point to each number as you count it.

0 1 2 3 4 5

Note for parent: Practise counting to five using your child's toys.

Numbers 1 to 5

Count the lily pads in the pond.
Colour them.

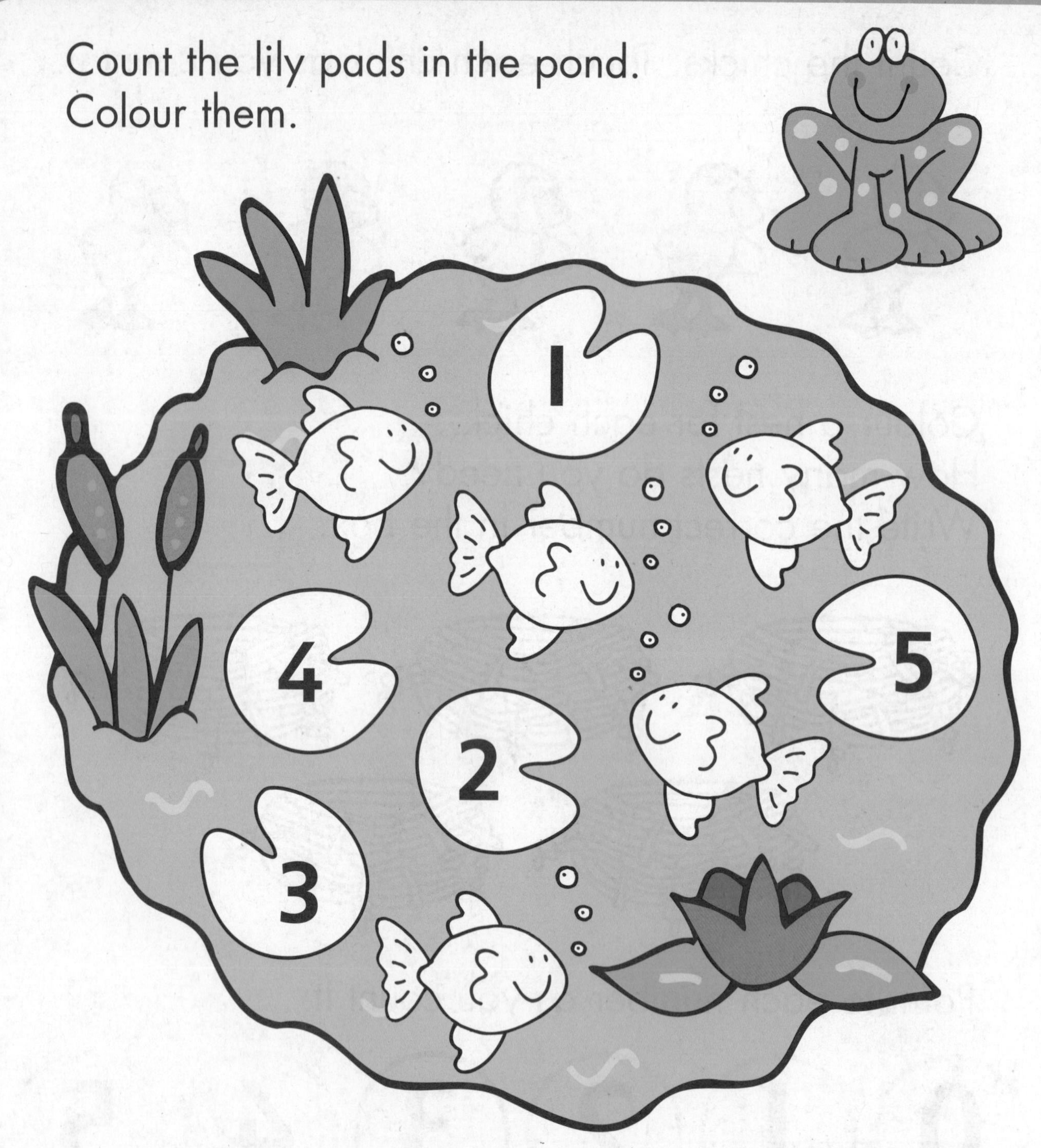

Now colour 5 fish friends for the frog to play with.

Note for parent: The numbers show your child how many objects (e.g. lily pads) are in the set.

Writing numbers 0 to 5

Start at the dot and follow the arrows to trace each number with a pencil. Read the number words.

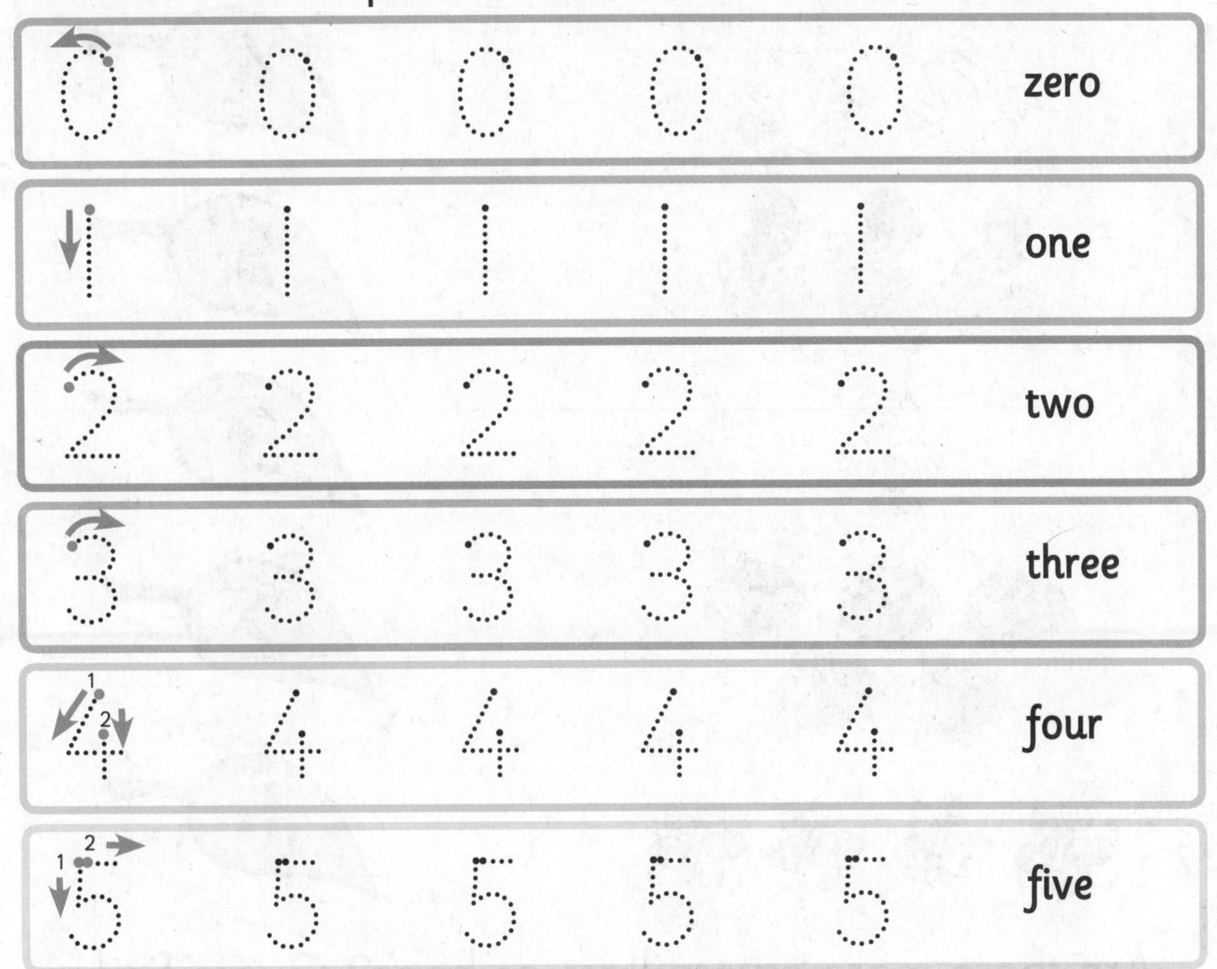

Write the missing number in each box.

Count and match

Count the animals in each set. Draw a line to match each set to the correct number.

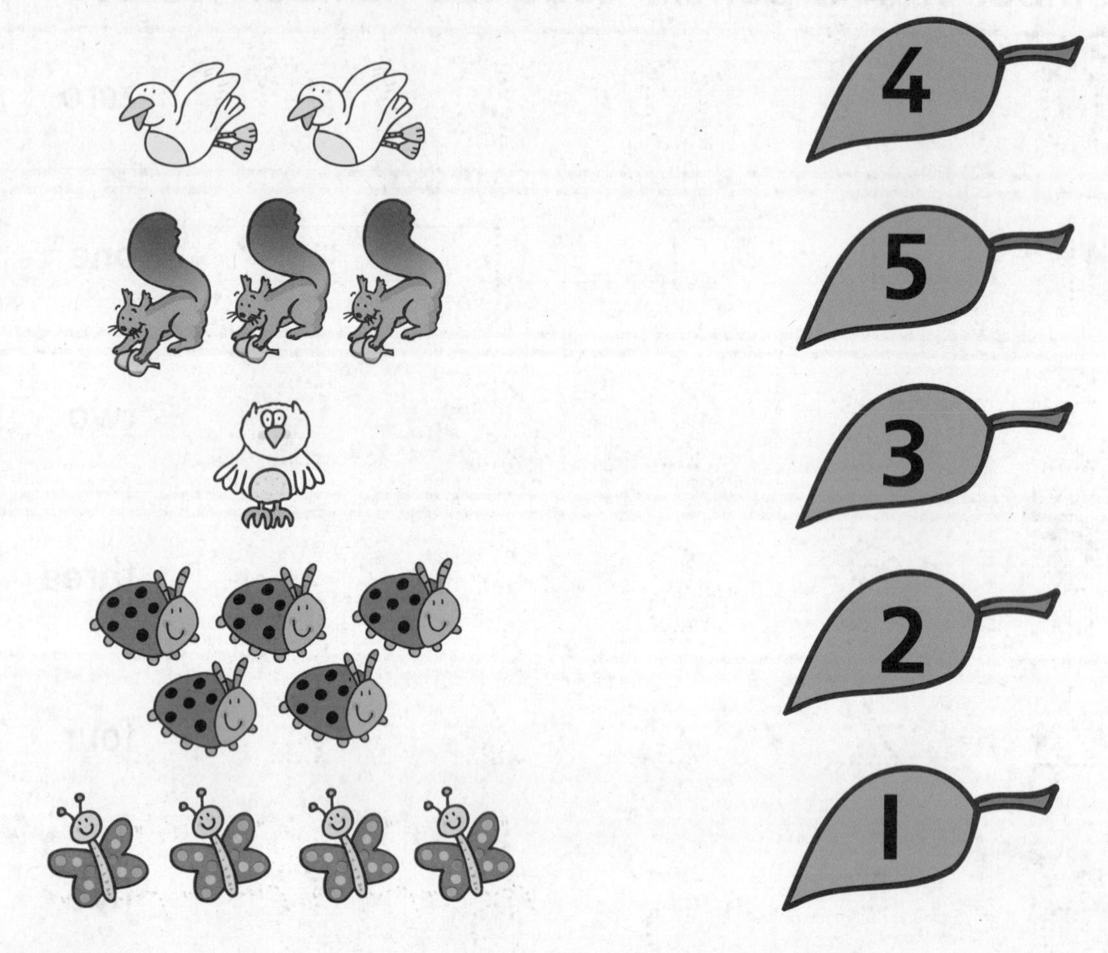

Are there more caterpillars or bees? Guess first, then count. Write the correct number in each box.

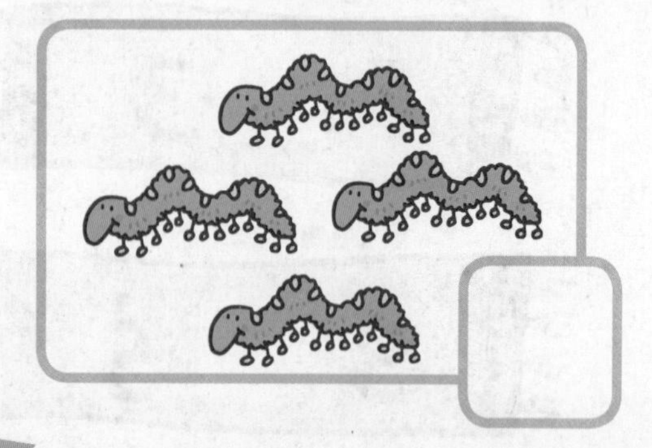

Note for parent: You can use language such as 'more' or 'less' to compare the numbers of animals. Ask: 'Are there more ladybirds or owls?' and 'Are there fewer butterflies or squirrels?'

Count the clothes in each row.
Circle the correct numbers.

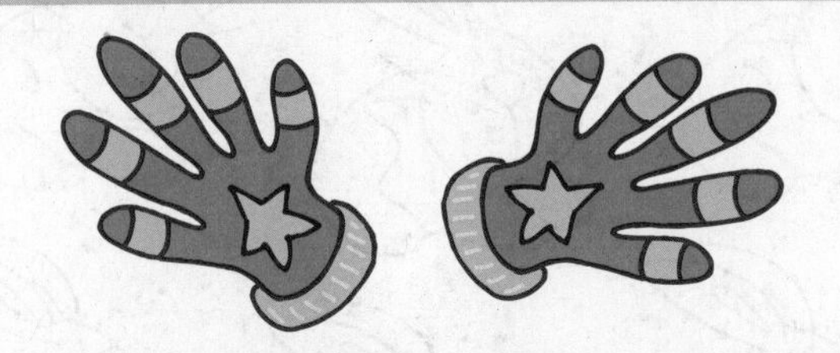

1 2 3 4 5

1 2 3 4 5

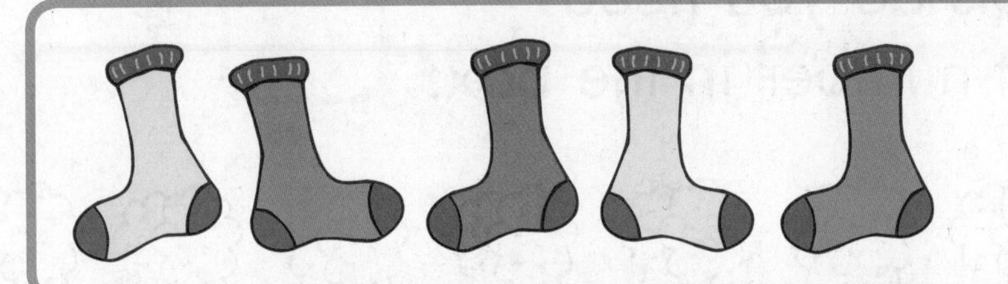

1 2 3 4 5

1 2 3 4 5

1 2 3 4 5

Note for parent: As a follow-up activity, count your child's clothes as you tidy them away. Sort them into groups of different colours and count how many there are in each group.

Counting up to 10

Count the rabbits. Touch each rabbit as you count it.

Colour a carrot for each rabbit.
How many carrots do you need?
Write the correct number in the box.

Point to each number as you count it.

1	2	3	4	5	6	7	8	9	10

Note for parent: Touching the objects as you count them reinforces the one-to-one relationship between the object and the number.

Writing numbers 6 to 10

Start at the dot and follow the arrows to trace each number with a pencil. Read the number words.

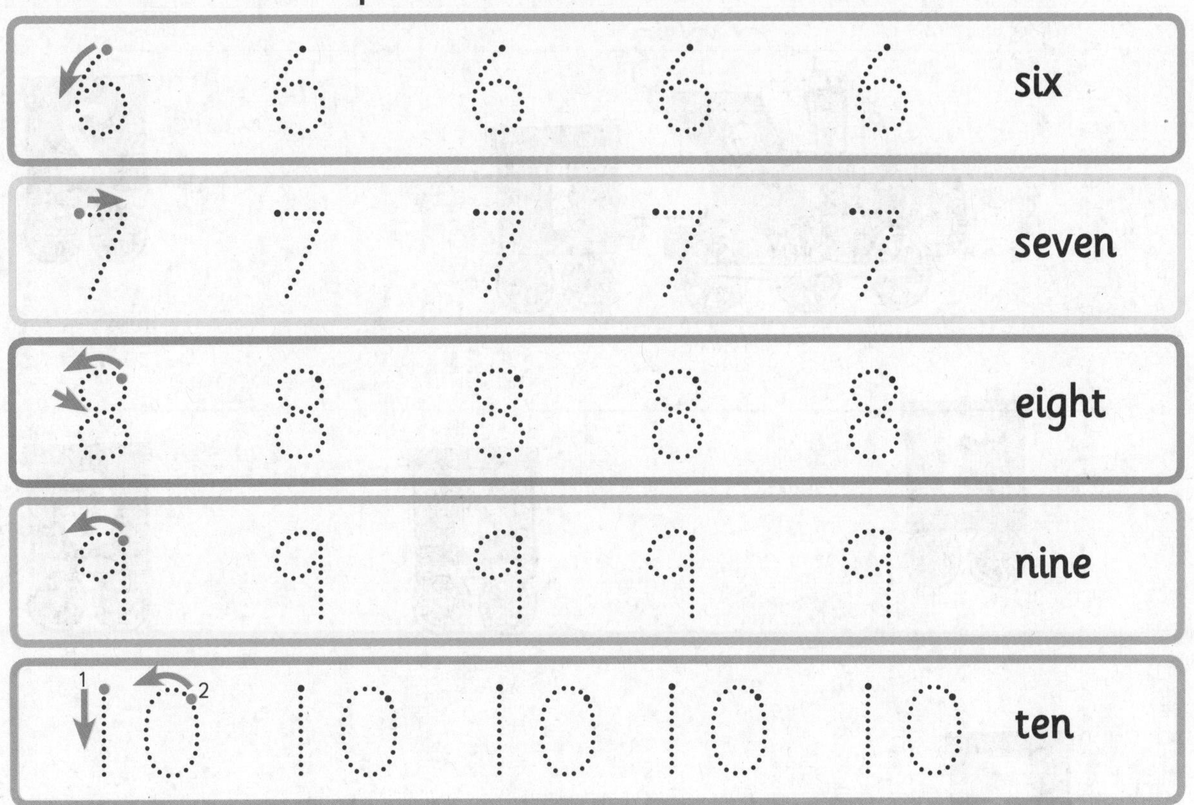

Write the missing number in each box.

Ordering numbers up to 10

Draw lines to join each train carriage to the next, in order from 1 to 10.

Note for parent: This activity provides practice in counting to 10 and the sequencing of numbers in the correct order.

Number 0 (zero)

Count the animals in each field.
Write the correct number in each box.

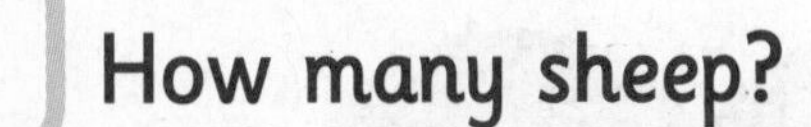

How many cows? ☐

How many lions? ☐

How many chickens? ☐

How many sheep? ☐

How many dogs? ☐

How many zebras? ☐

Note for parent: This activity helps to reinforce the concept of zero in a fun way.
Make up further 'silly' questions to which the answer will be zero.

Matching to a number line

Count the balloons in each group. Draw a line to match each group to the correct number.

Note for parent: Look at the position of the numbers on the line and ask questions. For example: 'Which number comes before 5?' and 'Which number comes after 5?'

6
7
8
9
10

Counting on

Count on from the numbers in each row.
Write the missing number on each sail.

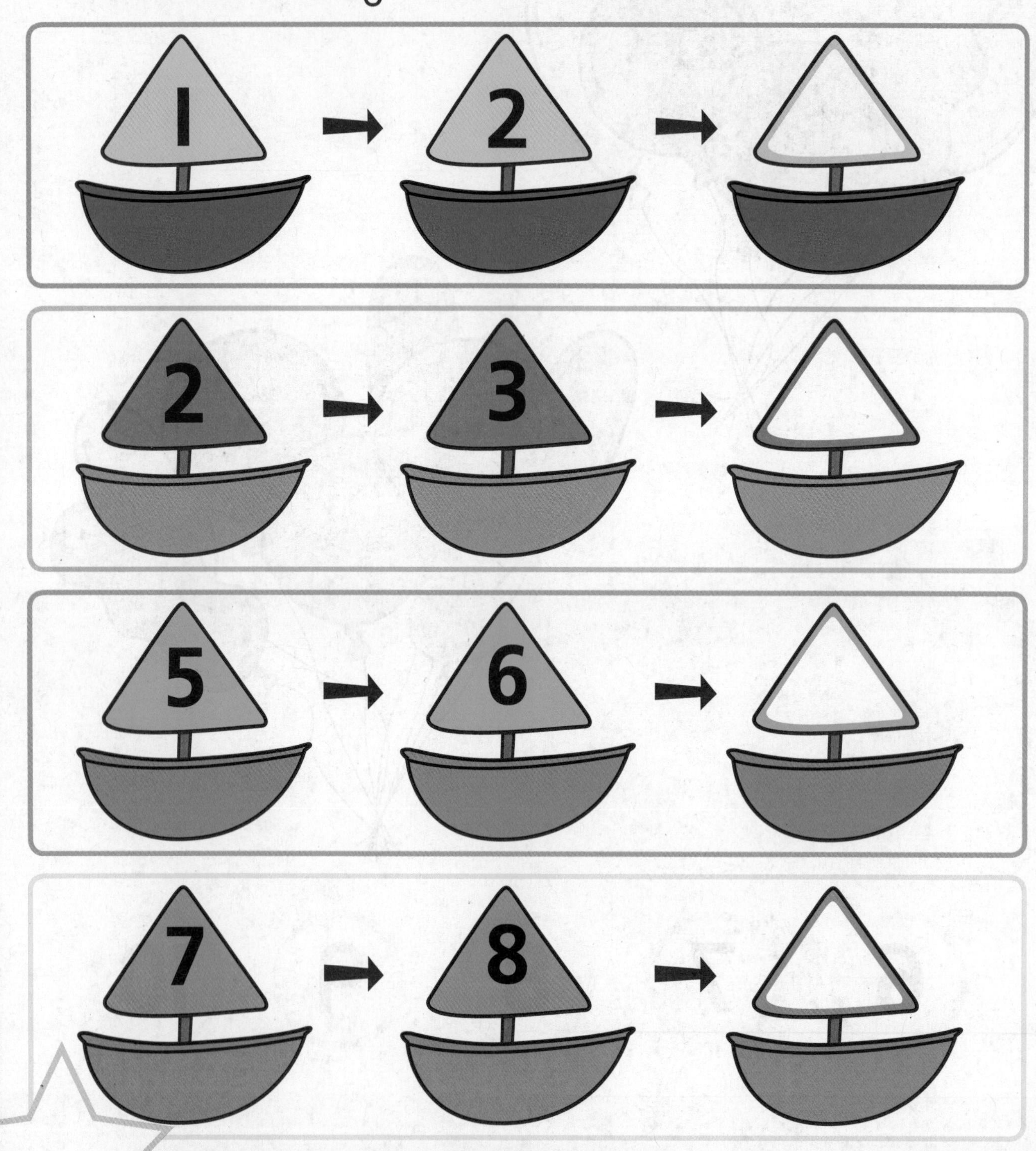

Note for parent: This activity provides practice in counting forwards from a number.
Think of further examples using numbers up to 10.

Counting back

Count back from the numbers in each row.
Write the missing number on each bus.

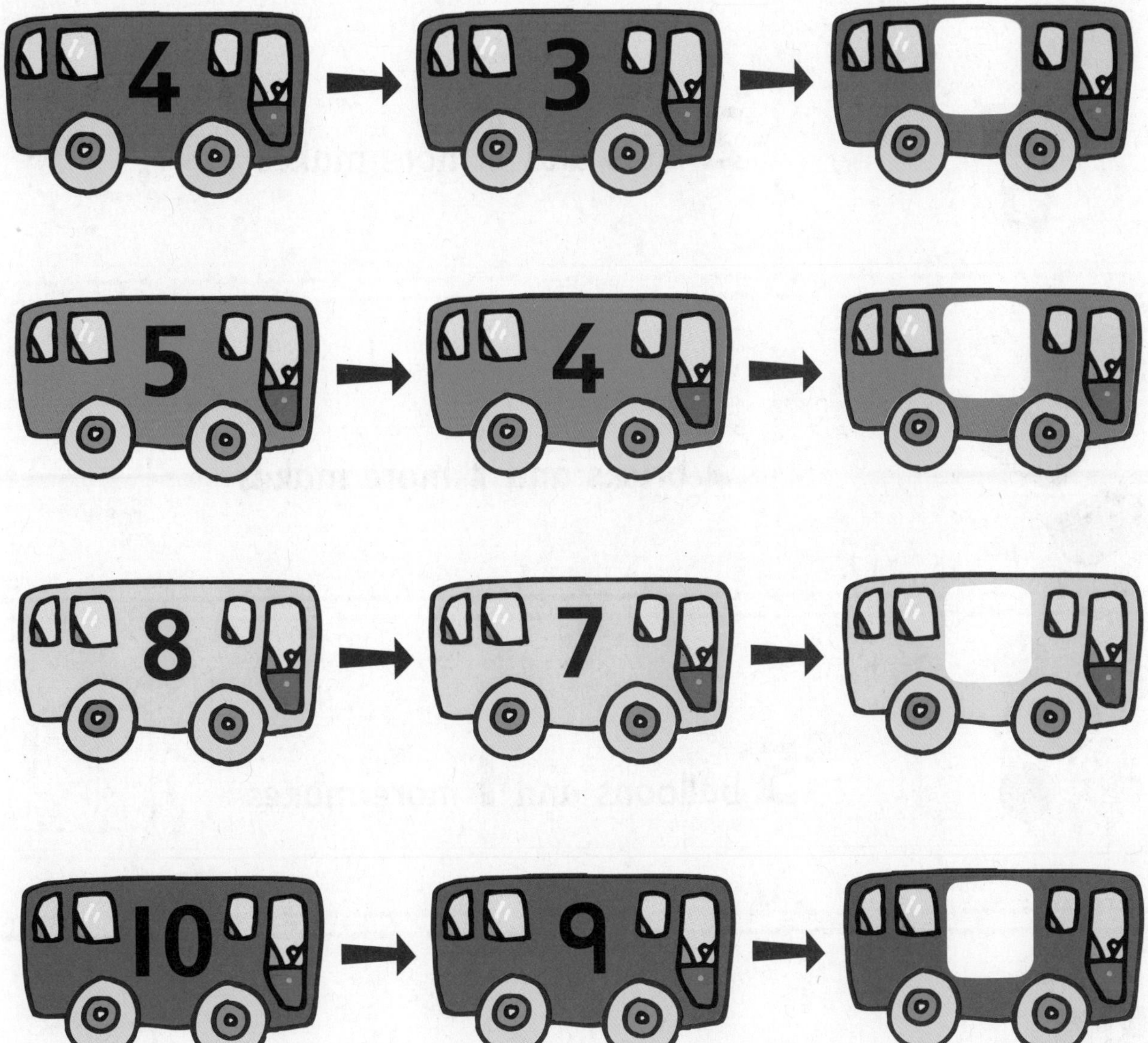

4 → 3 →

5 → 4 →

8 → 7 →

10 → 9 →

One more

Draw one more object in each row. Count how many objects there are altogether. Write the correct number in each box.

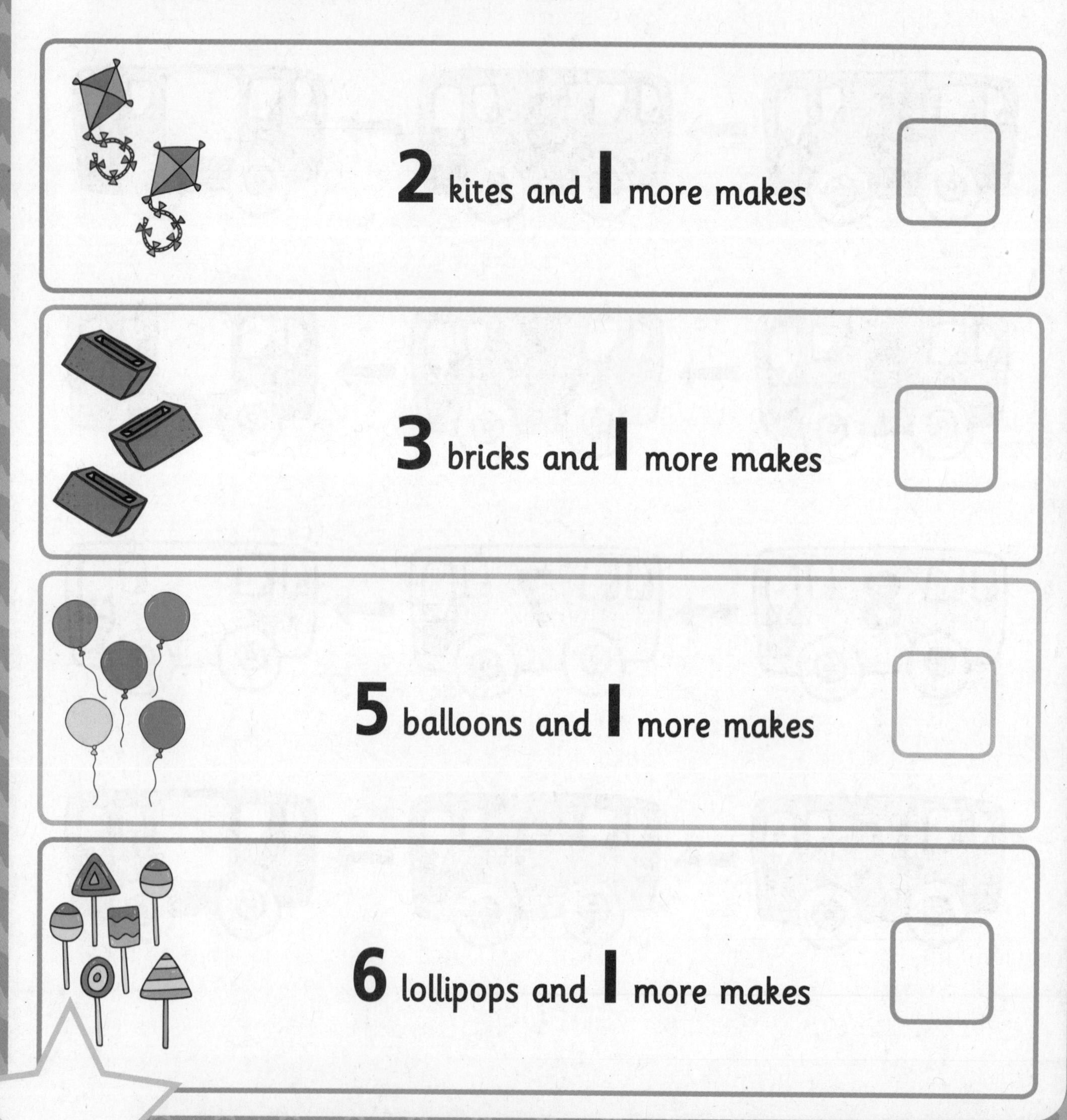

Note for parent: This activity introduces the concept of addition by drawing 'one more'. You can practise the addition of one more using groups of counting beads or buttons.

Two more

Count how many bananas there are altogether in each row. Write the correct number in each box.

Note for parent: When your child has grasped adding two more, try adding three more – again use counting beads or buttons.

Counting down from 5

Have fun counting and singing this song.

5 fat sausages sizzling in a pan,
All of a sudden, one went BANG!

4 fat sausages sizzling in a pan,
All of a sudden, one went BANG!

3 fat sausages sizzling in a pan,
All of a sudden, one went BANG!

2 fat sausages sizzling in a pan,
All of a sudden, one went BANG!

1 fat sausage sizzling in a pan,
All of a sudden, one went BANG!

No fat sausages sizzling in a pan!

Note for parent: Singing songs that have a counting element is a good way to reinforce number skills. Extend to larger numbers with 'Ten green bottles' and 'Ten in the bed'.

One less

Cross out one sweet treat on each plate.
Count how many are left on each plate.
Write the correct number in each box.

2 take away **1** leaves

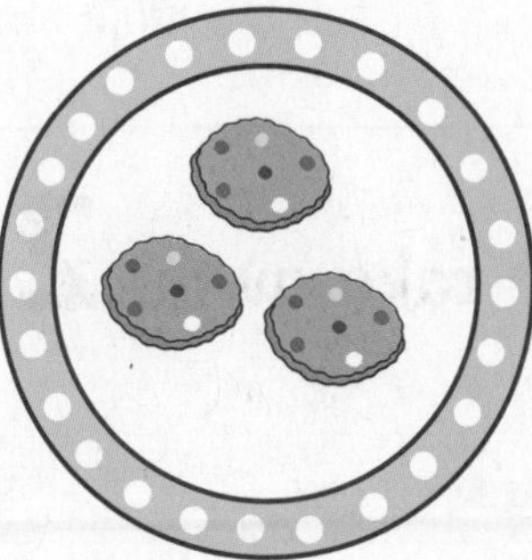

3 take away **1** leaves

5 take away **1** leaves

7 take away **1** leaves

8 take away **1** leaves

Note for parent: This activity introduces the concept of subtraction or 'taking away'.
Practise using real objects.

Two less

Cross out two pieces of fruit on each plate.
Count how many are left on each plate.
Write the correct number in each box.

2 take away **2** leaves

4 take away **2** leaves

5 take away **2** leaves

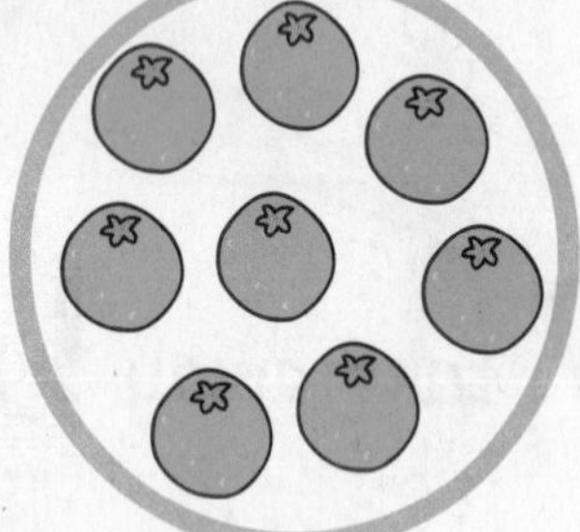

8 take away **2** leaves

9 take away **2** leaves

Note for parent: Show your child what subtraction means in a familiar context. For example, after a meal you might say: 'We had four bowls of ice cream – now there are none left!'

More or less

Who has more apples – Teddy or Robot? Guess first, then count. Write the correct number in each box.

Teddy has  apples. Robot has  apples.

Who has fewer oranges – Tom or Rob? Guess first, then count. Write the correct number in each box.

Tom has  oranges. Rob has  oranges.

Note for parent: Practise this activity using everyday objects. Ask: 'Do I have more pencils than you?' (Use two unequal groups of pencils to demonstrate the idea.)

Find and count

Count how many there are of each coloured snail.
Write the correct number in each box.

There are [ ] green snails.

There are [ ] yellow snails.

There are [ ] red snails.

Note for parent: Practise this activity using beads in three different colours.
Then ask your child to find out how many there are altogether.

Counting up to 15

Count the butterflies. Touch each butterfly as you count it.

Colour a flower for each butterfly.
How many flowers do you need?
Write the correct number in the box.

Point to each number as you count it.

1	2	3	4	5
6	7	8	9	10
11	12	13	14	15

Note for parent: This activity provides practice in counting to 15 and the sequencing of numbers in the correct order.

Sharing out

Emma and two of her friends are having a party.

How many drinks are there altogether? ☐

Tick the box if there are enough drinks for everyone to have 1 each. ☐

Note for parent: This activity introduces the concept of simple division – sharing something out so that each person has an equal amount.

How many cakes are there altogether? ☐

Tick the box if there are enough cakes for everyone to have 2 each. ☐

How many balloons are there altogether? ☐

Tick the box if there are enough balloons for everyone to have 3 each. ☐

Counting up to 20

Count the sheep. Draw a dot on each sheep as you count it.

Point to each number as you count it.

1	2	3	4	5	6	7	8	9	10
11	12	13	14	15	16	17	18	19	20

Note for parent: Drawing a dot on each sheep as you count it reinforces the one-to-one relationship between the object and the number.

Ordering numbers up to 20

Draw lines to join each duckling to the next, in order from 1 to 20.

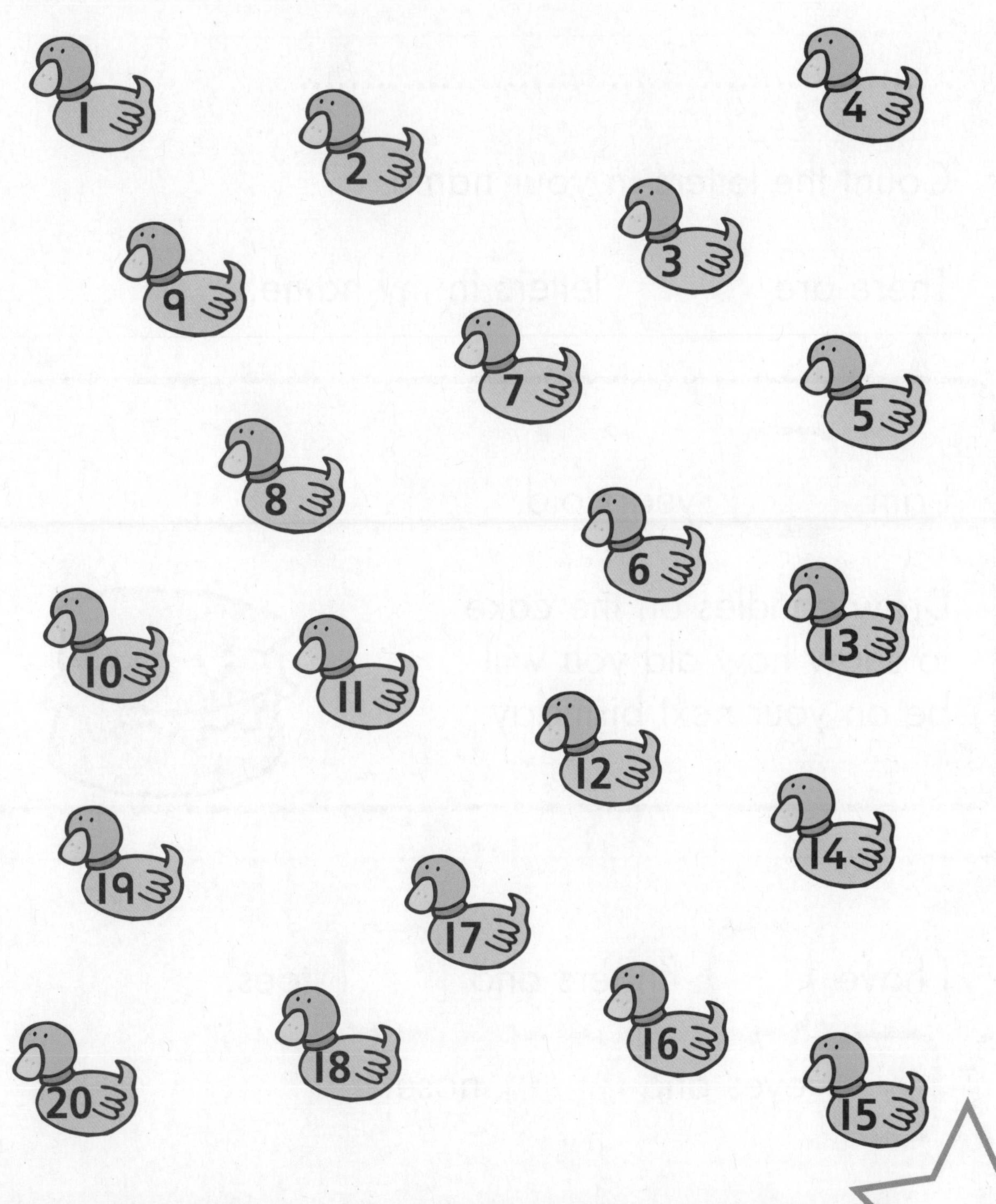

Counting me

Write your first name on the dotted line.

....

Count the letters in your name.

There are ☐ letters in my name.

I am ☐ years old.

Draw candles on the cake to show how old you will be on your next birthday.

I have ☐ fingers and ☐ toes, ☐ eyes and ☐ nose.

Note for parent: This activity encourages your child to use some of the numbers they have learned in a real context.

Draw a picture of yourself and your family here.

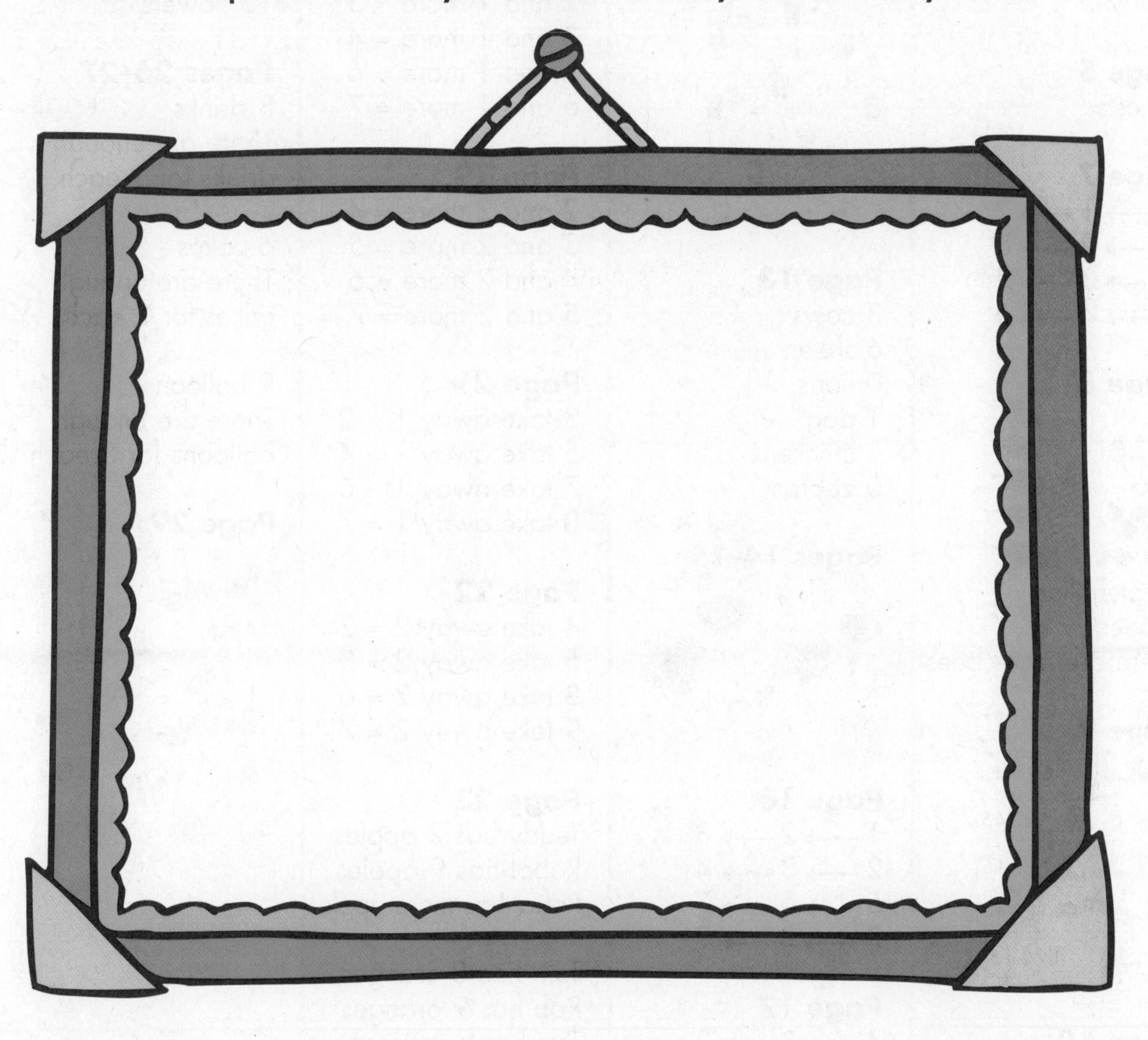

There are ☐ people in my family.

I can count up to ☐.

Answers

Page 4
3 bowls

Page 5
5 nests

Page 7

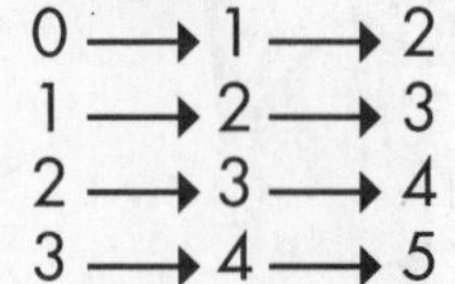

0 → 1 → 2
1 → 2 → 3
2 → 3 → 4
3 → 4 → 5

Page 8

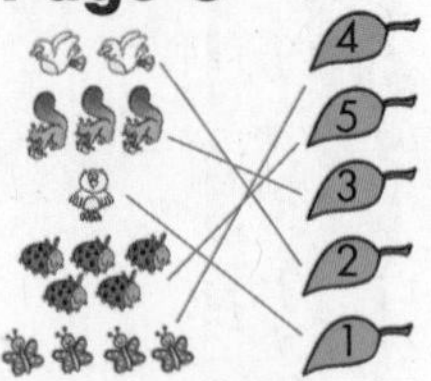

4 caterpillars
5 bees
There are more bees

Page 9

Page 10
10 carrots

Page 11
6 → 7 → 8
7 → 8 → 9
8 → 9 → 10

Page 12

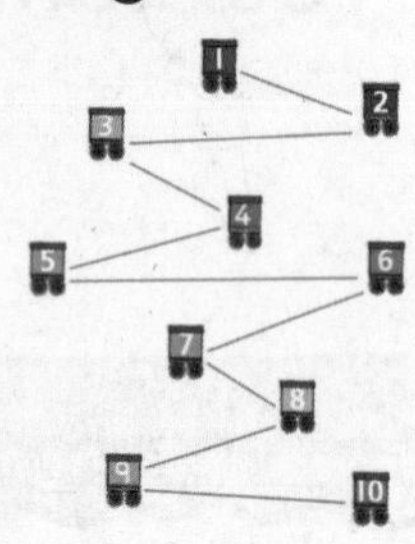

Page 13
3 cows
6 sheep
0 lions
1 dog
2 chickens
0 zebras

Pages 14–15

Page 16
1 → 2 → 3
2 → 3 → 4
5 → 6 → 7
7 → 8 → 9

Page 17
4 → 3 → 2
5 → 4 → 3
8 → 7 → 6
10 → 9 → 8

Page 18
2 and 1 more = 3
3 and 1 more = 4
5 and 1 more = 6
6 and 1 more = 7

Page 19
2 and 2 more = 4
3 and 2 more = 5
4 and 2 more = 6
5 and 2 more = 7

Page 21
3 take away 1 = 2
5 take away 1 = 4
7 take away 1 = 6
8 take away 1 = 7

Page 22
4 take away 2 = 2
5 take away 2 = 3
8 take away 2 = 6
9 take away 2 = 7

Page 23
Teddy has 7 apples
Robot has 9 apples
Robot has more apples

Tom has 8 oranges
Rob has 9 oranges
Tom has fewer oranges

Page 24
6 green snails
4 yellow snails
5 red snails

Page 25
15 flowers

Pages 26–27
3 drinks
There are enough drinks for 1 each 

6 cakes
There are enough cakes for 2 each 

9 balloons
There are enough balloons for 3 each ☑

Page 29

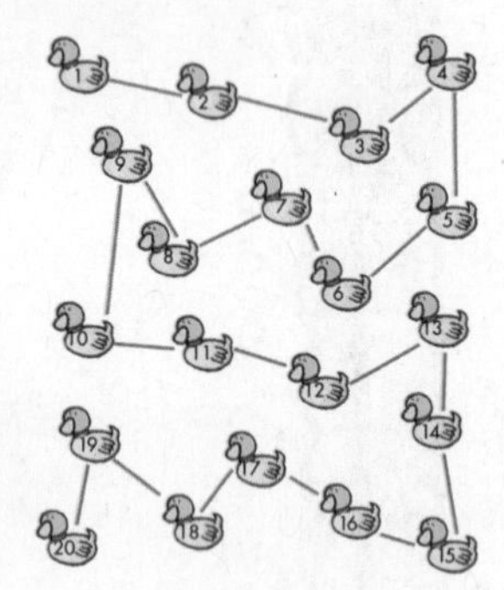